Made in America

Folk Art from the Shelburne Museum

A BOOK FOR SPECIAL DAYS

Pomegranate Calendars & Books
San Francisco

© 1988 Shelburne Museum, Shelburne, Vermont

Plate captions excerpted from *An American Sampler: Folk Art from the Shelburne Museum* published by the National Gallery of Art © 1987 Board of Trustees, National Gallery of Art. All rights reserved.

ISBN 0-87654-320-4
Pomegranate catalog number A520

For more information on Pomegranate's other publications, including day books, address books, calendars, art books, reproductions and fine art cards, please write to:

Pomegranate Calendars & Books
Box 980
Corte Madera, California 94925

Designed by Stephen Kruse
Printed in Singapore

Introduction

The Shelburne Museum is widely known for its superb collection of American folk art including quilts and coverlets, decoys, weather vanes, cigar-store figures, trade signs, carousel animals, scrimshaw, hooked rugs, whirligigs and other carvings. This book of days offers a rich selection of the Museum's finest folk art pieces.

The Shelburne Museum, located near the shores of Lake Champlain in northwestern Vermont, was founded in 1947 by Electra Havemeyer Webb to "show the craftsmanship and ingenuity of our forefathers." It grew out of Mrs. Webb's lifetime of collecting.

She was the daughter of "Sugar King" H.O. Havemeyer who, with his wife, Louisine, and her friend Mary Cassatt, formed one of the earliest and finest collections of European Impressionist and Old Master paintings. Electra inherited her parents' collecting urge, but her independent spirit led her in very different aesthetic directions.

Her mother was shocked when 18-year-old Electra brought home her first cigar-store Indian, purchased for $15 from a storekeeper in Stamford, Connecticut. "What have you done?" demanded the great collector of Degas, Monet and Manet. Electra could have backed down but instead answered, "I've bought a work of art." At the time few people would have agreed with her brave judgment of the Indian's artistic merit.

In 1910, Electra married J. Watson Webb, the son of Commodore Cornelius Vanderbilt's granddaughter Lila. Watson, a dashing young sportsman, introduced his wife to Vermont, where his father, Dr. William Seward Webb, maintained an enormous gentleman's estate on the shores of Lake Champlain in Shelburne. He also introduced her to the extravagant world of Long Island polo, his favorite sport, and, perhaps most importantly, to classic New England architecture.

By the early 1920s, Watson Webb was one of the greatest polo players in the world, and Electra was, in addition to her social duties on the polo circuit, the mother of five children; the mistress of estates in Shelburne and Westbury, Long Island, and a 17-room apartment on New York's Park Avenue; and her husband's companion on annual hunting trips to Alaska, Scotland and South Carolina.

Despite the range and complexity of her responsibilities, Mrs. Webb's collection continued to grow and grow. Dolls, toys, china, glass, quilts, primitive paintings and sculptures, hatboxes, costumes, tools, weather vanes, trade signs, rugs, furniture and scrimshaw jammed attics and spare rooms. Watson, wisely realizing that his wife's collecting habit was incurable ("Thank God there is no 'Collectors' Anonymous'," she once said) and that her collections might soon take over the house, finally had some extra rooms included for them in a new building which covered the indoor tennis court and pool.

"I kept on collecting," Mrs. Webb recalled in 1958, "I filled a house . . . our home, with collections, and my attic, of course, was a wonderful place. The sculpture increased over at the indoor tennis court, and as the children grew up, and somebody would ask for me, they would say, 'Oh, mother is over in the tennis court building with her junk.' "

Mrs. Webb began the Shelburne Museum in 1947 with one building and eight acres. Soon, however, she needed more space for her burgeoning displays. Stimulated by her husband's interest in New England architecture, she began to collect on a grander scale: she acquired whole buildings to decorate and fill. Many buildings were dismantled and reassembled at the Museum. Others, including the 220′ steamship *Ticonderoga* and the General Store, were moved intact.

Today, the Shelburne Museum consists of 37 exhibition buildings set in a 45-acre park. Shelburne's collections of American textiles, glass and ceramics, dolls, toys, pewter, furniture and other decorative arts are among the finest in the country. The Museum's collections of American paintings, prints and drawings are exceptional, too. There also are extensive and important collections of carriages and horse-drawn vehicles, American hand tools and early New England farming and homemaking implements.

Many structures were moved to Shelburne. Exhibit buildings include a wonderfully cluttered General Store, a one-room schoolhouse, six fully furnished early New England homes, a jail with stocks, an Adirondack hunting lodge, and a lighthouse from Lake Champlain. There is also a covered bridge, a variety of enormous barns, a steam train, a railroad station, a circus building and carousel, and four art galleries. In addition to things American, the Museum boasts an important collection of European art, including masterpieces by Rembrandt, Degas, Manet and Monet.

From the start, the Shelburne Museum reflected Mrs. Webb's eclectic enthusiasms and her wish to share her things with the public. It departed radically from the theories of other museums. Shelburne is neither a restoration nor a village, although it contains elements of both. The Museum is best seen as "a collection of collections," a very personal expression of one extraordinary woman's vision of American history and culture. In the words of one commentator, "Shelburne is unquestionably unique and is a work of art."

Robert Shaw
Shelburne Museum

Tree of Life, 1830
Cotton; appliquéd
Signed "Sara T.C.H. Miller/1830"

Textiles were considered an important part of the early American household inventory. Time consuming to produce and expensive to import, they often constituted a large percentage of a family's wealth.

1

2

3

4

5

6

7

Crimper: Double Eagle Head and Hand, c. 1840
Carved, incised ivory colored with red wax; brass and silver
$7^{7}/_{8} \times 4^{3}/_{16} \times 1^{3}/_{8}''$
Gift of George Frelinghuysen

For the thirty sailors aboard a whaling ship, life was both tedious and hard.
Monotony was relieved by such pastimes as gaming, fancy rope work, and
carving.

January

8

9

10

11

12

13

14

Rooster, c. 1890
Carved, polychromed wood
$16 \times 20^{1}/_{4} \times {}^{3}/_{4}''$
Attributed to James Lombard (b. 1865) of Bridgton, Maine

Weathercocks were probably the first vanes to move from the public perches of the European tradition (churches, meeting houses and civic buildings) to the American barn roof.

15

16

17

18

19

20

21

Cigar Store Indian with Hatchet, c. 1855
Carved, polychromed wood
$70^1/_2 \times 16^1/_8 \times 21''$
Attributed to John Cromwell (1805–73) of New York City; Cromwell
originated this design, which was copied by several later craftsmen.

Cigar-store figures were in use in America well before the Revolutionary
War, but they were not common until the mid-1800s. From about 1850 to
1900, thousands of cigar-store figures were made; during these years, no
respectable tobacconist kept shop without one.

22

23

24

25

26

27

28

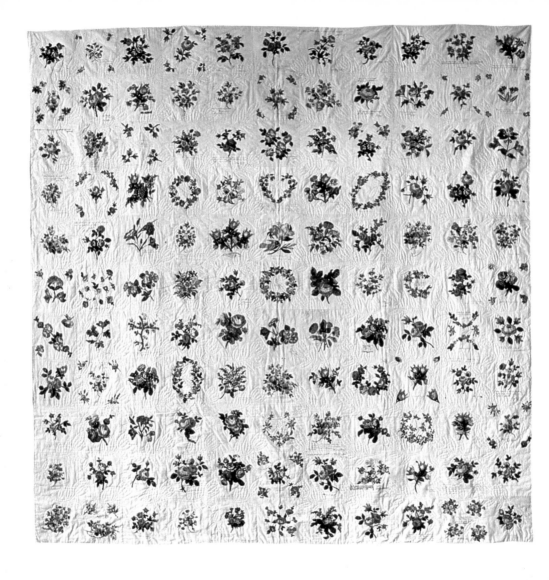

Cory Friendship/Chintz Album, 1852–1853
Cotton; appliquéd and pieced
93 × 93¹/₂″
Made for Reverend Benjamin L. Cory by the parishioners of the
Presbyterian Church in Perth Amboy, New Jersey. Gift of Mr. Willard
Kiggins, a Cory descendant.

Jan./Feb.

29

30

31

1

2

3

4

Canada Goose, c. 1849
Carved, polychromed wood, brass plates and pin
$11^{1}/_{2} \times 24 \times 11^{1}/_{8}''$
Attributed to Charles C. Osgood (1820–1886) of Salem, Massachusetts.
The removable head is attached to the body by a pair of interlocking,
pinned brass plates. Gift of Mrs. P. H. B. Frelinghuysen

*Wildfowl decoys, made to lure game birds within shooting range, have been
used by American hunters for centuries. The Indians originated the idea in
response to the abundance of the continent's wild game.*

5

6

7

8

9

10

11

Squirrel Cage, c. 1900
Carved, sawn, and turned, polychromed wood with iron rods and
iron nails
$26 \times 24 \times 8^{1/2}''$

*The whimsical squirrel cage undoubtedly was made for a child's amuse-
ment. The four jointed figures worked their up-and-down saws to the rhythm
of the pet squirrel's antics on the center treadmill; nesting boxes on either
side of the treadmill housed the animal(s) during periods of inactivity.*

12

13

14

15

16

17

18

Tavern Sign (front), c. 1870
Sawn and turned polychrome wood
$30 \times 33^{3}/_{4} \times 3^{1}/_{4}''$

As taverns sprang up along main traffic routes, their brightly painted signs
alerted passersby that food, drink and lodging were available within. These
signs usually featured a strong image, such as the sun depicted on one side
of the E. Noyes tavern sign.

19

20

21

22

23

24

25

Star of Bethlehem, c. 1850
Wool and cotton; pieced and quilted
73 × 71$^{1}/_{2}$″
Made by Mrs. Emile (Marie) Marin of Saint Pie, Quebec

The tradition of pieced work quilts evolved from the early settlers' need for thrift. Small pieces of fabric cut from worn clothing or bedcovers were joined or seamed together in a predetermined pattern to create a larger textile.

26

27

28   29

1

2

3

4

Cow, c. 1870
Hammered sheet iron
$24^{1}/_{2} \times 36^{3}/_{4} \times 1^{3}/_{4}''$
Found in Hardwick, Vermont

March

5

6

7

8

9

10

11

Swift, c. 1850
Turned and incised whale ivory and bone; wood padded with velvet
$19^{1}/_{2} \times 8^{1}/_{16} \times 8''$
Gift of George Frelinghuysen

The scrimshander could use a wide variety of materials to make yarn swifts. The basket ribs on this swift were shaped from the whale's jaw bone, while teeth were used for the yarn holder, lower clamp, and spool holders. The center shaft was turned from a long walrus tusk, and the sewing box built from wood veneer.

12

13

14

15

16

17

18

Goat, before 1903
Carved polychromed wood with glass, leather, brass and iron attachments
$55^{1}/_{2} \times 66 \times 12''$
Made by Gustav A. Dentzel Carousel Company of Philadelphia; carved by Daniel Muller (1872–1952)

The German-born Dentzel opened the first carousel manufacturing business in America in 1867. Dentzel's shop produced the most realistic and graceful of all carousel animals; his carvers paid enormous attention to anatomical detail, and his painters rendered every nuance of the animal's coloration.

19

20

21

22

23

24

25

Tulips and Orange Slices, c. 1850
Cotton; appliquéd and quilted
95 × 95″
Found in Kingston, Massachusetts

26

27

28

29

30

31

1

TO⟩TE—Indian Hunter, c. 1860
Polychromed sheet iron
$51 \times 31 \times \frac{1}{16}''$
TO⟩TE stands for "Totem of the Eagle," an emblem of the Improved
Order of Redmen, an early American fraternal organization. Found in
Pennsylvania.

*Because weather vanes were made to be seen only from a distance,
silhouetted against the sky, their forms emphasize essential features.
Proportions were often exaggerated for effect and clarity; note the Indian's
oversized, misplaced eye and tiny hands and feet.*

2

3

4

5

6

7

8

Captain Jinks, c. 1880
Carved, polychromed wood, with iron rods and stamped, painted tin placards
75×17×17″
Shop of Samuel A. Robb (1851–1928) of New York City; attributed to Robb's associate Thomas J. White. This is a caricature of Robb in his National Guard uniform.

Although a few cigar-store figures were still in use into the 1920s, demand for them was sharply reduced after the turn of the century, largely due to the introduction of electric signs which could advertise a business after dark.

9

10

11

12

13

14

15

Pair of Parrots, c. 1875
Carved, polychromed wood
Each $7^{1}/_{2} \times 3^{1}/_{4} \times 2''$
Made by Wilhem Schimmel (1817–1890), Cumberland Valley,
Pennsylvania; Gift of Mrs. D. W. Bostwick

All Schimmel's carving was done with a pocket knife, using blocks of pine.
Knife marks were smoothed with worn pieces of glass before painting.
Schimmel used ordinary oil-based household paint, often in vivid colors. He
probably drew his paint supply from the dregs of leftover tins, which may help
to explain the oddness of some of his color combinations.

April

16

17

18

19

20

21

22

Schoolhouse Border Coverlet, 1851
Cotton and wool, Jacquard-woven tied double cloth
97 × 89"
Woven by Jacob Witmer, Manor Township, Lancaster County,
Pennsylvania

*Jacquard coverlets were introduced in the early nineteenth century. Because
of their elaborate floral and mosaic patterns, they were advertised as
"fancy" coverlets to differentiate them from handwoven pieces with geometric
patterns. The Jacquard loom attachment, mounted over a handloom, was a
sophisticated device that controlled the pattern by the use of punched cards.*

April

23

24

25

26

27

28

29

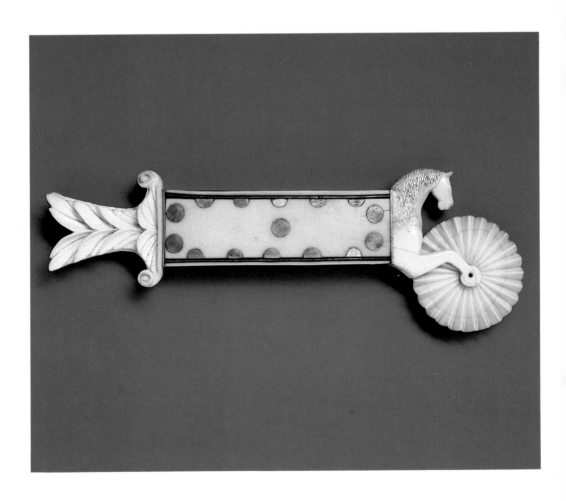

Crimper: Horsehead with Phoenix Tail, c. 1850
Carved, incised ivory with lamp black, inlaid with rosewood, silver,
ebony, and bronze
$2^{11}/_{16} \times 7^{5}/_{8} \times ^{3}/_{4}''$
Gift of George Frelinghuysen

*The pie crimper was the most popular of the kitchen implements fashioned
by scrimshanders. The crimper's intricate rosette zig-zag wheel and fork,
used to cut, press and pierce pie pastry provided the scrimshander with an
opportunity to demonstrate both carving and design skills.*

30

1

2

3

4

5

6

Fish with Flag Sign, c. 1850
Sawn and polychromed wood with polychromed iron flag
$34 \times 60^{1}/_{2} \times {}^{3}/_{4}''$
Found in central New York State

Medieval inn signs often employed emblems of trade guilds to attract members of a specific profession. Fish, for example, represented the guild of boatmen and fishermen, while flags were often found on tavern signs located near military headquarters. The fish and flag sign *may have been used at an inn located near a naval yard.*

7

8

9

10

11

12

13

Mariner's Compass, 1835
Cotton; pieced, appliquéd and quilted
98¾ × 96″
Made in New Jersey

May

14

15

16

17

18

19

20

Swan, c. 1910
Carved, polychromed wood
$20^3/8 \times 35 \times 11^3/4''$
Made by John Holly, Jr. (1851–1927) or William Holly of Havre de
Grace, Maryland (1845–1923)

May

21

22

23

24

25

26

27

Spinning Woman Whirligig, c. 1875
Carved, polychromed wood with iron attachments
$26^3/_4 \times 22^1/_2 \times 22^1/_2''$
Used as a trade sign in Salem, Massachusetts

A close relative of the weather vane is the whirligig, a figural device powered by wind. This figure, which apparently served as a trade sign, spun wool at the wheel and moved her foot up and down on the treadle. The speed of her work depended entirely on the prevailing winds.

May/June

28

29

30

31

1

2

3

Seabury Bedrug, 1819
Handspun wool yarns sewn to wool ground
93 × 101″
Made by Dorothy Seabury of Stowe, Vermont. Signed, "John &
Dorothy Seabury, Stowe, March 1819." Gift of Robert J. Whiting, a
Seabury descendant

The bedrug was made by embroidering multiple strands of handspun yarn
in a looped running stitch on one side of a ground fabric, to create a
deep pile. Dorothy Seabury used newly woven cloth as a ground for her
embroidery work.

June

4

5

6

7

8

9

10

Lion, before 1903
Carved polychromed wood with glass, leather, brass and iron
attachments
$59 \times 65 \times 12''$
Made by Gustav A. Dentzel Carousel Company of Philadelphia; carved
by Daniel Muller (1872–1952)

*The major carousel companies employed a number of professional craftsmen.
Patterns for animals were usually designed and drawn by one of the master carvers. The carpenters then assembled basic block forms of the body,
head, and legs by pegging and gluing a number of pieces of wood together.*

June

11

12

13

14

15

16

17

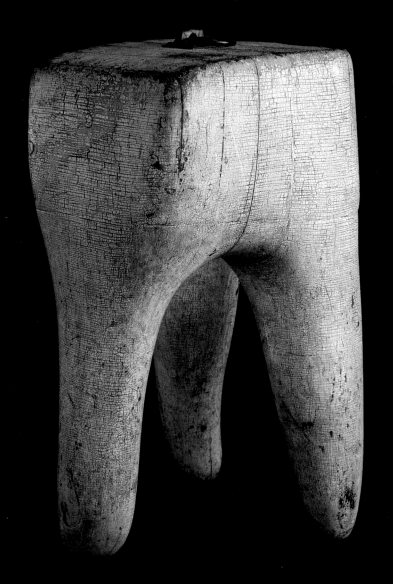

Dentist's Sign, c. 1850
Carved, polychromed wood
$22^3/_4 \times 12^1/_4 \times 11^1/_2''$
Gift of Julius Jarvis

Trade signs symbolizing the goods or services offered were typically oversized replicas of such actual objects.

18

19

20

21

22

23

24

Eagle Candlewick Counterpane, c. 1862
Multistrand cotton yarn, cotton; embroidered
$81^1/_2 \times 85^1/_4''$
Signed, "Done by Myrtilla Newman, Dixfield, M [Massachusetts] 62."
Gift of Mr. J. Watson Webb, Jr.

25 _____

26 _____

27 _____

28 _____

29 _____

30 _____

1 _____

Sperm Whale's Tooth, c. 1850
Incised and inked ivory
$1^{7}/_{8} \times 3^{1}/_{2} \times 7^{5}/_{8}''$
Gift of George Frelinghuysen

*The simplest and most familiar form of scrimshaw is the whale tooth
decorated with engraved scenes recording the whale chase and capture.
Sometimes portraits of famous figures or designs were copied from popular
illustrations.*

July

2

3

4

5

6

7

8

Circus Equestrienne, c. 1885
Hammered, gilded sheet copper filled with lead, on wrought iron pivot
$39^{1}/_{4} \times 34^{1}/_{2} \times 1^{1}/_{4}''$ with swinging extension of $5^{1}/_{8} \times 30 \times 32''$
Found in Massachusetts

July

9

10

11

12

13

14

15

Tree of Life Counterpane, late 18th century
Cotton and linen; appliquéd
$106 \times 103''$

16 _____

17 _____

18 _____

19 _____

20 _____

21 _____

22 _____

Scottish Highlander, c. 1878
Carved, polychromed wood
$89 \times 20 \times 25''$
Shop of Samuel A. Robb (1851–1928) of New York City

With the introduction of snuff around 1700, the Scottish highlander entered the permanent repertory of cigar-store figures.

July

23

24

25

26

27

28

29

Pair of Willets, c. 1900
Carved, polychromed wood with iron nails wrapped with sheet lead
$7^{1}/_{2} \times 13 \times 2^{1}/_{2}''$
Found in Connecticut

White settlers were quick to take note of Indian hunting methods, which, like the abundance of game, were entirely new to them. The decoy, crafted from wood to ensure permanence, soon became an essential part of their hunting gear. By 1840 the wooden decoy was firmly established in American hunting tradition.

30

31

1

2

3

4

5

Basket of Flowers, c. 1840
Cotton; reverse appliqué
$74 \times 73^1/_2''$
Gift of Mrs. John C. Wilmerding

*Bedding was always the first and most important group of textiles acquired
for the household, and decorative bedcovers were highly prized as a way to
cheer a sparsely furnished house.*

6

7

8

9

10

11

12

Butterfly, c. 1880
Pierced, cut and polychromed sheet copper
$19 \times 27^{1}/_{2} \times ^{1}/_{16}''$
Manufactured by unknown company

While extremely detailed realism could be achieved using molded copper, not all manufactured vanes were so complex: the simple silhouette butterfly is a form that was offered with small variations by several manufacturers.

August

13

14

15

16

17

18

19

Eagle on Uncle Sam's Hat, c. 1870
Carved, polychromed wood
$24 \times 11 \times 23^{1}/_{4}''$
Found in Pittsburgh, Pennsylvania, where it was used as a sign outside
a veteran's boarding house

August

20

21

22

23

24

25

26

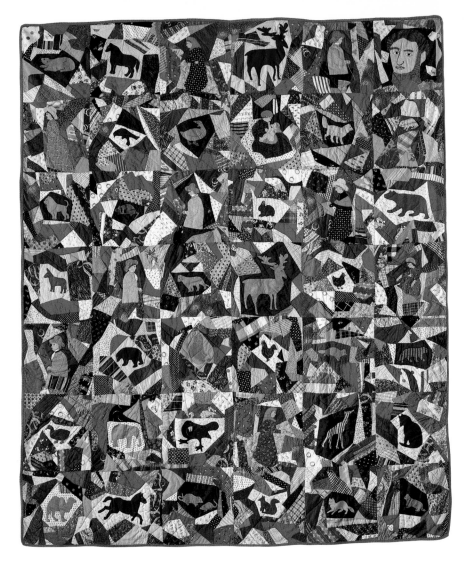

Haskins Family, c. 1870
Cotton; pieced, appliquéd and embroidered
$69^{1}/_{2} \times 83''$
Made by Mrs. Samuel Glover Haskins of Granville, Vermont

27

28

29

30

31

1

2

Gen.¹ STARK

AT BENNINGTON.

E. NOYES.

Tavern Sign (back), c. 1870
Sawn and turned polychrome wood
$30 \times 33^{3}/_{4} \times 3^{1}/_{4}''$

The mounted figure of the revolutionary war hero General Stark on the reverse side of the E. Noyes tavern sign follows in a long European tradition of knights and soldiers depicted on signboards. General Stark led a militia of New Hampshire and Vermont troops at the Battle of Bennington in the Revolutionary War.

September

3

4

5

6

7

8

9

Tiger, before 1903
Carved, polychromed wood with glass, leather, brass, and iron
attachments
$50 \times 80 \times 14^{1}/_{2}''$
Made by Gustav A. Dentzel Carousel Company of Philadelphia; carved
by Daniel Muller (1872–1952)

*Heads and legs of carousel animals were usually carved first and then
attached to the body block for finish work. Although the basic forms were set
by the patterns, each carver brought his own style to the detailing of saddlery,
tack, musculature, and mane.*

September

10

11

12

13

14

15

16

Locomotive, c. 1860
Sheet zinc, brass rod, iron pipes, and iron bars
22×44×3″
Used on a railroad station in Providence, Rhode Island; the sunburst
lightning rod is probably a later addition.

17

18

19

20

21

22

23

Ann Robinson Counterpane, 1814
Cotton and linen; appliquéd and embroidered
$98^3/_4 \times 93^1/_4''$
Signed, "Ann Robinson, October 1, 1813, finished January 27, 1814."

*Appliqué patterns tend to be more pictorial and representational than pieced
ones, which are not laid out on a ground, because the quiltmaker is allowed
greater flexibility in arranging the pattern pieces.*

24

25

26

27

28

29

30

Black Duck, c. 1920
Carved, polychromed wood
$7^1/_2 \times 15^1/_2 \times 5^3/_4''$
Made by A. Elmer Crowell (1862–1952) of East Harwich,
Massachusetts

October

1

2

3

4

5

6

7

George Washington on Horseback, c. 1780
Carved, polychromed wood, and leather
$21^{1}/_{2} \times 7 \times 20''$
Attributed to a "Mr. Coolidge"; found in Andover, Massachusetts

October

8

9

10

11

12

13

14

Mariner's Compass, before 1852
Cotton; pieced and quilted
94 × 90″
Made by Mary Canfield Benedict of Arlington, Vermont

October

15

16

17

18

19

20

21

Massasoit, Indian Chief of the Wampanoag, c. 1885
Hammered, polychromed sheet copper with lead solder
$30^{5}/_{8} \times 30^{1}/_{4} \times 2^{3}/_{4}''$
Harris & Co., Boston, Massachusetts

Some exaggeration is used in the design of this vane (note the enormous arrow tip), but the figure's proportions are generally realistic, and the molded three-dimensional construction allows attention to surface details of the costume and features.

22

23

24

25

26

27

28

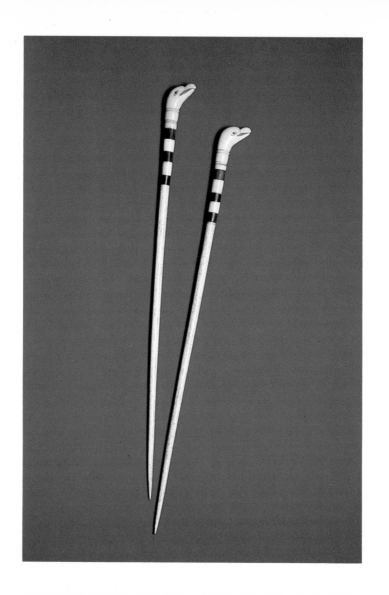

Knitting Needles: Eagles' Heads, c. 1850
Carved, incised ivory and bone, red wax and rosewood; walrus ivory
heads and whale bone shafts
$1 \times {}^{7}/_{16} \times 12{}^{3}/_{4}''$
Gift of George Frelinghuysen

Sailors employed carved whale bone combined with such materials as
tortoise shell, horn, pewter, silver, or wood to fashion kitchen implements,
domestic and needlework tools, and fashion accessories.

29

30

31

1

2

3

4

Indian with Pipe, c. 1885
Carved, polychromed wood
$75^3/_4 \times 20^1/_2 \times 22''$
Made by Louis Jobin (1845–1928) of Quebec

Most figures were mounted on bases, often equipped with wheels so they could be easily moved outside the shop in the morning and back in at night for protection from vandalism.
Louis Jobin, Canada's renowned carver of religious tableaux, began his career crafting figureheads and trade figures.

November

5

6

7

8

9

10

11

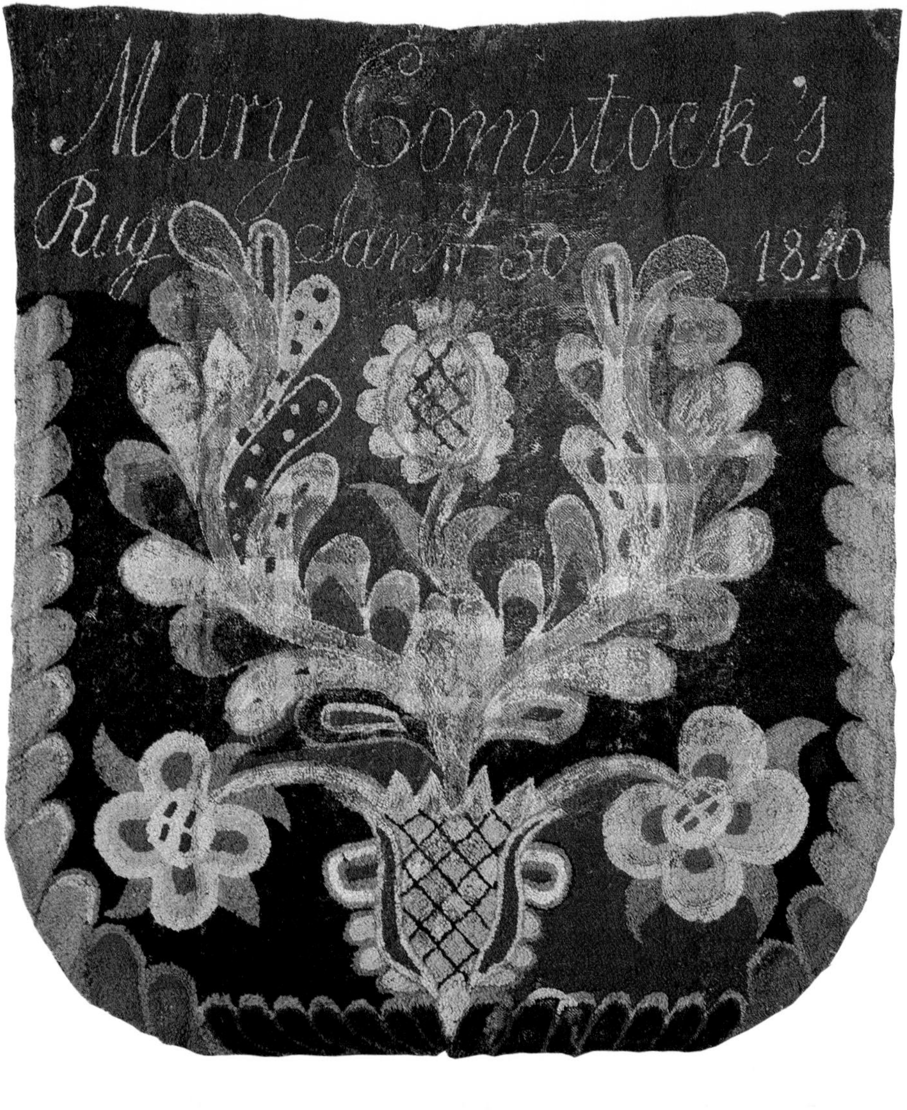
Mary Comstock's
Rug Jany 30 1810

Mary Comstock Bedrug, 1810
Handspun wool yarns sewn on handwoven twill-weave wool blanket
84¼ × 76″
Made by Mary Comstock of Shelburne, Vermont. Signed, "Mary Comstock's Rug, Jany 30, 1810." Gift of Mrs. Henry Tracy.

Mary Comstock recycled a lovely handwoven plaid twill blanket for the ground fabric of this bedrug.

12

13

14

15

16

17

18

Clock Shop Sign: Eagle with Watch, c. 1875
Carved, polychromed wood with iron hook and iron reinforcements
$30^1/_4 \times 40^1/_4 \times 30''$
Used by watchmaker John Gordon of New London, Connecticut

Prior to the advent of general public education and literacy in the late eight-
eenth century, proprietors relied on carved and painted signs to supply a
strong visual message to the public. The purpose of the signs was not only to
interpret their trades or services, but also to attract business.

19

20

21

22

23

24

25

Horse, before 1903
Carved polychromed wood with glass, leather, brass, and iron attachments
$59 \times 65 \times 12''$
Made by Gustav A. Dentzel Carousel Company of Philadelphia, Pennsylvania; carved by Daniel Muller (1872–1952)

Most of Dentzel's figures were grouped in threes with the largest and most elaborate animal on the outside in order to draw riders onto the carousel. The right or "romance" side of these outer row figures always received special attention from the carver.

26

27

28

29

30

1

2

Chintz Album, c. 1840
Cotton; appliquéd and quilted
80×108″
Made by Mrs. Ridgley of Baltimore

3

4

5

6

7

8

9

Mermaid, c. 1850
Carved, polychromed wood
$22^{1}/_{2} \times 52^{1}/_{2}''$
Found in Wayland, Massachusetts, at the homestead of Warren Gould
Roby

December

10 _____

11 _____

12 _____

13 _____

14 _____

15 _____

16 _____

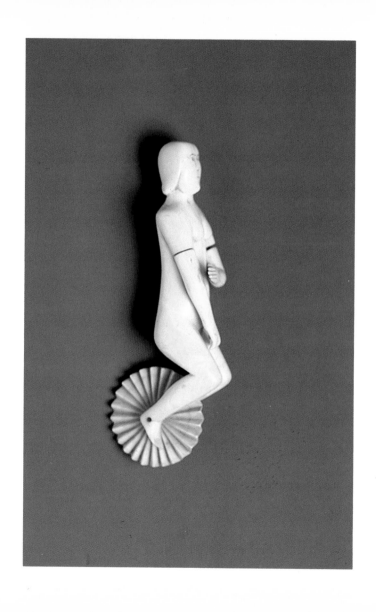

Crimper: Woman Riding Wheel, c. 1850
Carved and inked ivory
$4^7/_8 \times 1^7/_8 \times 1^1/_2''$
Gift of George Frelinghuysen

Handles of pie crimpers could be pierced with hearts and flowers copied from
embroidery or quilt patterns or carved with designs inspired by such images
of the sailor's everyday world as the ship's compass or figurehead.

17

18

19

20

21

22

23

Leopard Rug, c. 1880
Wool fabric hooked on burlap ground
$37^1/_4 \times 70^1/_2''$

*Hooked rugs allowed a rugmaker to recycle scraps of fabric into useful and,
often, beautiful floor coverings. The pile surface was made by using a hook
to pull a narrow cloth strip up through a coarsely woven foundation fabric
in a series of loops. The closeness of the loops determined the density and
durability of the finished rug.*

December

24

25

26

27

28

29

30   31